SINGALONG
SONG BOOK

First published in Great Britain by HarperCollins Children's Books in 2009

1 3 5 7 9 10 8 6 4 2
ISBN: 978-0-00-731978-7

A CIP catalogue record for this title is available from the British Library.

Based on the television series **Big & Small**.

Composers: Douglas John Cameron and Jack Lenz
Lyricist: Andrew Bernhardt
Singers: Lenny Henry and Imelda Staunton

Big & SMALL™

SINGALONG
SONG BOOK

HarperCollins *Children's Books*

The Big And Small Song

It doesn't matter if you're tiny or tall,
It doesn't matter if you're Big or Small...

If you want to have fun it doesn't matter at all.
You got it, Big!
Why thank you, Small!

Skipping, flipping, climbing up a rope,
Hiding, riding, sliding down a slope,
Skating on an ice cube, swinging on a star,

It makes no difference what size you are!

Nice!

If you want to have fun it doesn't matter at all,
'Cause here we are,
We're Big and Small!

Yeah!

Give Me Yes!

I've got the place all to myself,
No-one's the boss of me.
I'm going to have such fun today
It's great to be so free.

I'm going to do what I want, yeah!
It's my lucky day,
To do what I want just when I want
So Big please stay away.

It's going to be great today,
It's going to be a big success,
Don't give me no or stop or woah
Just give me yes, yes, yes!

Don't get me wrong, I think Big is great
But I won't miss him at all.
I'll be so busy having fun, yeah!
I'm going to have a ball.

It's going to be great today,
It's going to be a big success,
Don't give me no or stop or woah
Just give me yes, yes, yes!
Don't give me no or stop or woah
Just give me yes, yes, yes!

Party Time!

Party time! Party time!
I'm getting ready for party time!

Step one,
Go for it Small!

Yeah! Got to get on, I've got to send
An invitation to every friend.

Party time! Party time!
I'm getting ready for party time!

Step two,
Give it up for Big!

No time to wait or hesitate,
String up the streamers, let's decorate.

Party time! Party time!
I'm getting ready for party time!

Step three,
Let's hear it for the cake!

Oven's hot and ready, it's time to bake,
Yummy hot muffins and a big scrummy cake.

Party time! Party time!
I'm getting ready for party time!

Step four,
Hey! That's the door!

Yeah! Door starts knocking, so let them all in!
Get the room rocking, let the fun begin.

Party time! Party time!
I'm getting ready for party time!

Let's Go Outside

Let's go outside and see the world so wide,
So much to discover out there.
It's good to get out, stride out and step out,
Hit the road, Small, and sniff that fresh air.

Look we're in luck, I can see a duck
Who's leading her friends on a stroll.
There'll be quacking and skimming on the water that's brimming
Down at the old waterhole.

Let's go outside and see the world so wide,
So much to discover out there.
It's good to get out, stride out and step out,
Hit the road, Small, and sniff that fresh air.

Check out that horse, he's happy of course,
He's out jumping fences for fun.
Oh he'll gallop and trot until he gets hot,
Frolicking free in the sun.

It's good to get out, stride out and step out,
Hit the road, Small, and sniff that fresh air.

Do They Dig It? They Do!

Do they dig it?
They do.
Do they dig it?
Oh yes they do.

Dig down, deep down,
Down through the ground.

Shift those shovels,
Digging to the sound.

Now do they dig it?
Well, they do.
Let me hear it, do they dig it?
Oh yes they do.

Little holes, big holes,
Any hole will do.

Just keep on digging,
Until the digging is through.

Do they dig it?
They do.
Do they dig it?
Oh, oh yes they do.
Oh yes they do.

The Clog Barn Dance

I got my clogs on and I'm gonna dance,
I got my clogs on and I'm gonna dance,
I got my clogs on and I'm gonna dance,
Right round this old barn.

Ferret's in the jam jar, cat's in the box,
Chicken's in the saucepan dancing in his socks,
Dog's in the rocking chair fishing for a boot
But I just want to dance, hey!

I got my clogs on and I'm gonna dance,
I got my clogs on and I'm gonna dance,
I got my clogs on and I'm gonna dance,
Right round this old barn.

Frogs at the back door croaking in a line,
Rabbit's on a skateboard doing mighty fine,
Donkey doing nothing, just watching with a grin
But I just wanna dance, hey!

Woo Hoo! Yee Ha! Woo Hoo! Let's get clogging!

I got my clogs on and I'm gonna dance,
I got my clogs on and I'm gonna dance,
I got my clogs on and I'm gonna dance,
Right round this old barn.
Right round this old barn, hey!
Right round this old barn! Yee ha!

Mysterious Woods

Hup - two - three - four,
March it up - two - three - four.

Mysterious woods, mysterious woods
We're coming to find our ball,
And I'm not scared at all
You're just some trees and birds and bees.

Was that a tiger's call?

Hup - two - three - four,
March it up - two - three - four.
Hup - two - three - four,
March it up - two - three - four.

Mysterious woods, mysterious woods
We've come to find our ball,
And here come Big and Small
We'll search the trees on hands and knees.

We'll peer and poke and crawl.

Hup – two – three – four,
March it up – two – three – four.

Mysterious woods, mysterious woods,
We're coming to look around,
And when the ball is found
We'll march some more and shout and roar.

Just listen to our sound.

Nurse Small

I'm aching and shaking,
And feeling so bad,
But Small is the best nurse
That I've ever had.

He's caring, he's sharing,
He's such a great nurse.
It's really quite tempting
To start feeling worse.

My hot brow needs mopping,
He's right on the case,
He's back in two seconds,
And dabbing my face.

He's caring, he's sharing,
He's such a great nurse.
It's really quite tempting
To start feeling worse.

I'm sneezing like crazy,
My throat is so sore,
But Small is my hero,
Could I ask for more?

He's caring, he's sharing,
He's such a great nurse.
It's really quite tempting
To start feeling worse.

A story's what I need
Don't give me that look,
Just sit down beside me
And read from this book.

Gwelfs Are Real!

Gwelfs are real.

I don't think so!

I just know so!
But I'm oh so sure!
I'm so sure.

That Gwelf's been knocking on our door,
It wants to meet us, don't you ignore it.

Gwelfs aren't real, I'll show you, look!
You'll only find them in your book.

Gwelfs are real.

I don't think so!

I just know so!
But I'm oh so sure!
I'm so sure.

I don't want to spoil your fun,
But I've never seen a single one.

Well, come with me, I know I'm right,
Here at last! A Gwelf! Tonight!

Gwelfs are real.

I don't think so!

Ha! I just know so!
But I'm oh so sure!
I'm so sure.

Tall Small

Yes Small is my name but let me explain,
There's something that I've got to do.
It may not be wise but I'm changing my size
And hey! Just think of that view!

Tall will be great, when I'm standing up straight,
The whole world will look up to me.
Next time you drop by, if you want to say 'Hi!'
You'll just have to climb up a tree.

I'm stretching myself, I'll look down on an elf,
I'll make that worm eat her words.
And just for a laugh, I'll outgrow a giraffe,
And I'll be up there with the birds.

Tall will be great, when I'm standing up straight,
The whole world will look up to me.
Next time you drop by, if you want to say 'Hi!'
You'll just have to climb up a tree.

It's Better With Two

The sky's full of snow, and there's nowhere to go but I'm happy,
'Cause my piano and me, we make great company, I'm so happy.

But! One is OK but when I want to play,
I'd rather have two, say, someone like you.
One can be fun but two makes a pair.
And a game made for two is fun you can share.

It's better with two!

I paint and I draw, and it's never a bore, 'cause I'm happy
To be just with me, it's OK you see, 'cause I'm happy...

But! One is OK but when I want to play,
I'd rather have two, say, someone like you.
One can be fun but two makes a pair.
And a game made for two is fun you can share.

It's better with two!

I Can Paint You, You Can Paint Me

We'll paint just anything that we can see,
I could paint you and you could paint me.

I'll paint the woodpile, you paint some logs.

I'll paint those lilies if you paint those frogs.

We'll paint just anything that we can see,
I could paint you and you could paint me.

So many choices, now where to begin?

Here, have a wipe Small, you've got paint on your chin.

We'll paint just anything that we can see,
I could paint you and you could paint me.

You paint that flower and I'll paint that tree.

You paint that bird, and I'll paint that bee.

We'll paint just anything that we can see,
I could paint you and you could paint me.

You paint those clouds and I'll paint that sky.

Ah, the clouds won't keep still!

Ah, but it's worth a try...

We'll paint just anything that we can see,
I could paint you and you could paint me.

Friends Forever

Whenever we're together, life's just better, life's just fine.
We're forever buddies, need a hand?
Just take mine.

When you cut that hose... (oh yeah!)

And how we made it rain... (that was amazing!)

That tomato nose... (that was funny!)

And that crayon down the drain...

When I lost my 'saur... (I'm still sorry about that)

And hiding 'neath the bed...

When I made your door... (still love that door!)

Making stuff inside the shed.

Whenever we're together, life's just better, life's just fine.
We're forever buddies, need a hand?
Just take mine.
Just take mine.

All Aboard for Dreamland

Dreamland, dreamland,
All aboard for dreamland,
Our dreamboat's set to sail, across a cloudy moon.
All aboard for dreamland
Our dreamboat's leaving soon...

When it's time to go to bed
I try to sleep and snore,
But I know there'll be no dreamland,
If I can't have my dear old dinosaur...

Dreamland, dreamland,
All aboard for dreamland,
Our dreamboat's set to sail, across a cloudy moon.
All aboard for dreamland,
Our dreamboat's leaving -
All aboard for dreamland,
Our dreamboat's leaving soon.